find out about farm animals

Written and edited by
Paul Harrison
and Moira Butterfield

Designed by
Chris Leishman

Illustrated by
Rachael O'Neill

Contents

Chrysalis Children's Books

All about farm animals

Animals are kept on farms because they provide food, wool and skins.

Leather is made from the skins of cows and pigs.

Milk comes from cows, goats and sheep.

Meat comes from cattle, sheep, pigs and farm birds such as hens, geese and turkeys.

Eggs are collected from farm hens, ducks and geese.

Fun Fact

About 580 thousand million hens' eggs are laid every year.

Knitting wool is made from the coats of sheep.

From farm to factory

Farm products are taken to factories and made into many different products.

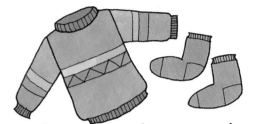

Wool is used to make clothes.

Skins are made into leather goods.

Dairy products are made from milk.

3

Different farms

Farm animals and farm buildings are different around the world.

Some farms around the world are very small. The farmers only keep enough animals to feed their own families.

Fun Fact

Some Australian sheep farms cover many thousands of kilometres.

They are so big that the farmers must use aeroplanes to travel around them.

Farms with lots of meadows are ideal for grass-eating animals such as cows.

Some farms are high on mountainsides. Only a few animals, such as goats, can live here.

Farm food

Most farmers grow some food for their animals. For instance, they may grow, cut and store grass to make **hay**.

In **winter** the farmer gives the stored food to the animals.

5

Cows

Cows are usually kept in groups called herds. Some herds are kept for milking. Others are kept to produce beef.

A dairy cow stores milk in its **udder**.

Suction cups squeeze the cow's teats.

Udders are sprayed to keep them clean.

Feeder

A **dairy cow** is a female. It produces lots of milk. The farmer milks the cow twice a day.

Cows have four stomachs. Two are for storing food and the other two for digesting food.

Milk is collected in **recording tanks**.

The milk is stored and chilled, ready to go off to the **dairy**.

Milk goes from the recording tanks to one large **receiving tank**.

Milk

Milk is added to many foods that are made in factories. Here are some examples:

Ice cream

Chocolate

Instant puddings

Biscuits

Instant soup

Sheep

Sheep like to live outdoors. Their woolly coats keep them warm.

In summer sheep live in fields or on hillsides. They eat grass.

In winter the sheep are kept near the farm.

In summer sheep are dipped in disinfectant to kill any insects living on them.

A group of sheep is called a **flock**.

Crook for catching sheep

A **sheepdog** helps to round up the sheep.

A female sheep is called a **ewe**. A male sheep is called a **ram**.

Shearing

Each summer the sheep are sheared. Even though it looks painful it doesn't actually hurt and it keeps the sheep cool in the summer sun.

Electric clippers

A whole coat is called a **fleece**.

The fleeces are packed in big woolsacks. They are sold to make wool.

9

Pigs

Pigs provide bacon, pork and ham. Their bristles are used to make paintbrushes. Pigs can be kept outside in fields or inside pig pens.

Warm dry bedding

Duroc pig

Hampshire pig

Water trough

Pigs use their noses to root around the ground for food. They eat both meat and plants.

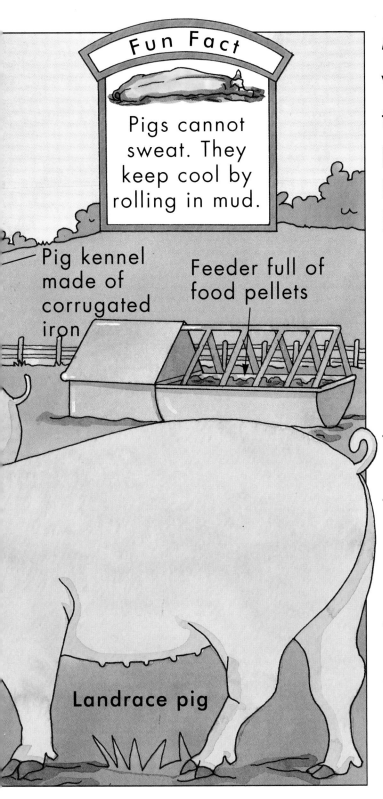

Pigs cannot sweat. They keep cool by rolling in mud.

Pig kennel made of corrugated iron

Feeder full of food pellets

Landrace pig

Mums and babies

When a pig is about to have babies it is put in a **farrowing pen** away from other pigs.

Ten or twelve piglets may be born at once. They are called a **litter**.

A female pig who has had babies is called a **sow**.

11

Farm birds

Chickens provide eggs and meat. On some farms they can go outdoors whenever they want, but on other farms they are kept in cages.

A **henhouse** provides a warm, safe place for free-range hens to lay eggs.

Light Sussex

Chickens use their hard beaks to peck for food.

Big birds

Ducks lay bigger eggs than hens. They need a farm pond to paddle in.

Chickens kept in cages are called **battery** hens.
Outdoor chickens are called **free-range** chickens.

White Leghorn

Bantam

Rhode Island Red

Hens are female chickens. They lay eggs. **Cockerels** are male chickens. They have long tail feathers.

Geese make good watchdogs because they honk loudly if anyone comes near.

Turkeys are kept for their meat.

Small farm animals

Goats are some of the smallest animals kept on farms.

Goat **paddocks** need high fences as goats can jump up to heights of 1.5m.

Female goats are called **nannies**.

Male goats are called **billies**. They have beards and shaggy coats.

Baby goats are called **kids**.

Saanen goat

Some goats are kept on mountainsides. They are looked after by a kind of shepherd called a **goatherd**.

Goats are kept mostly for their milk but some long-haired goats provide wool as well.

Smaller still

Rabbits are mostly kept for meat. Angora rabbits provide wool, too.

Some farmers keep **bees** for the honey that they make.

Farmers often keep **cats** to kill the mice and rats that eat crop stores.

Horses

Horses once did all the heavy work on farms. They are still used in many parts of the world.

Horses are used to round up cattle and sheep in America and Australia. They are called **stock horses**.

The largest horses are called **draught horses**. They are still used in ploughing competitions.

Collar

Strong body

Long 'feather' hair around the feet

Chains attached to the plough

Donkeys and mules

In some countries **donkeys** and **mules** work on farms.
They are strong and sure-footed.

Donkey

A mule is a cross between a horse and a donkey.

Mule

Around the world

Different kinds of farm animals are kept around the world.

In Africa, **ostrich** are bred for their meat and feathers.

In northern parts of the world people get meat and milk from their herds of **reindeer**.

In Peru, South America, people farm **llamas** and **alpacas**. The shaggy coat of the alpaca is good for making wool. Llamas provide meat and milk.

Alpaca

In China, **water buffalo** plough the paddy fields where rice is grown.

Llama

Unusual farms

Some farmers keep very unusual animals. Here are some examples:

Snails are kept for food.

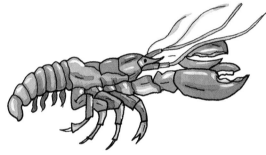

Lobsters are bred underwater.

Snakes' venom is used in medicine.

19

Animal babies

Farm animal babies are often born in spring or summer when the weather is warmer than in winter.

Farmers often put out bales of hay for **lambs** to play on.

Growing **chicks** are kept in an outdoor **run**.

Lambs are often born as twins.

The covered part of the run has bedding straw in it.

When **ducklings** go for a swim they follow their mother in a line.

Lambs drink their mother's milk. This is called **suckling**.

Ewes recognize their own lambs by smell and sound, even amongst hundreds of sheep.

Hen eggs must be kept warm so that chicks will **hatch**. They peck their way out about three weeks after the eggs are laid.

Newly hatched chicks are kept warm under a heat lamp.

Feeding babies

Calves are kept indoors and fed from buckets until they are strong enough to go outside.

Sometimes **ewes** do not look after their **lambs**. These lambs have to be handfed with bottles of milk.

Wild farm animals

Some wild animals live on farms. They often come out at dawn or dusk, when it is quiet and safe.

Foxes raid bins at night, and may even try to take chickens!

Owls often find cosy places to nest in farm buildings.

Brown rats eat farm grain stores.

House mice eat the grain in barns. Harvest mice eat the crops growing in the fields.

Bats sometimes roost in barn roofs.

Wild rabbits like to eat young crop shoots.

Wild hare

Harvest mouse

Field animals

Not all wild farm animals live in farm buildings. Animals such as dormice, shrews, hedgehogs and birds live in the **hedgerows** that surround the fields.

As farms get larger, the hedgerows are cut down to make space for larger fields or more crops. Then these animals lose their homes.

23

Index

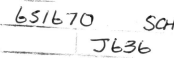

Senior Editor Nicola Wright
Series concept Tony Potter
Design Manager Kate Buxton
Production Zoe Fawcett
Printed in China

ISBN 1 84238 661 8

10 9 8 7 6 5 4 3 2 1

This edition first published in 2003 by
Chrysalis Children's Books
The Chrysalis Building, Bramley Rd, London W10 6SP

Copyright © Chrysalis Books PLC

24